The Town Boy

Mr Jones' nephew Thomas is a true city boy – until he gets to know Little Red Tractor and his friends!

Put the stickers in the right places to tell the story of Thomas' first day in Babblebrook.

"Good morning Little Red Tractor!" grinned Stan as he stepped out of his farmhouse. Little Red Tractor tooted and whirled his crank handle in the sunshine to say good morning too.

Little Red Tractor wondered what exciting adventures he and Stan would have that day. There was never a dull moment in Babblebrook!

...ny and Ryan raced into
...e yard.

"Is Thomas here yet?"
...ked Amy.

...Mr Jones' nephew was due
...arrive that morning from the
...y, and they couldn't wait to
...ow him around.

"Climb aboard," said Stan,
pointing to Little Red Tractor's
trailer. "We can all go and
meet him together."

"Toot! Toot!" parped Little
Red Tractor, as they chugged
off to Beech Farm.

...fortunately, over at Beech
...rm, Thomas and Mr Jones
...n't seem to be having a very
...od time.

"Babblebrook smells. I want to
...y on the computer," grumbled
...omas, running indoors.

"I don't think Thomas likes the countryside," Mr Jones explained when everyone arrived. "He's going to need time to get used to things now his mum and dad have moved here."

At last Thomas stopped playing 'Speed Bikes' on the computer and came outside. He didn't look very happy to see everyone.

"Stumpy's got a quad bike," smiled Amy, trying to be friendly. Thomas finally looked interested.

Stan invited Thomas to come and meet Stumpy and Nipper, his quad bike. Thomas frowned at Little Red Tractor's old trailer, but climbed in.

"Oh! Now my sweatshirt's all dirty," he sighed as they headed off.

Over at the windmill, Stumpy was fixing Nipper.

"The back wheel's gone all wobbly," he explained to Elsie. She rolled her eyes. She'd seen Stumpy's fixes before!

Stan needed to stop and feed his cows on the way to the windmill.

"Are you going to help us Thomas?" he asked, lifting a bag of fodder out of the trailer. Thomas didn't look keen.

"You're not frightened of a si old cow are you?" said Ryan

"Me! Frightened? Huh!" scoffed Thomas, but inside felt very frightened indeed.

Amy gently patted one of the cows. "Look. She likes it."

Thomas slowly reached out his arm and gave the cow a stroke. She felt much nicer than he had imagined. He was actually starting to enjoy himself!

"Race you back to Little Red Tractor!" said Ryan.

It was time to go and see Stumpy. In the scramble poor Thomas skidded in a cow pat, falling flat on his bottom. "Eeuurggh!" he cried at the nasty mess.

Elsie and Stumpy were full of smiles when they spotted Little Red Tractor chugging up the lane.

"You must be the new arrival!" said Stumpy, as Thomas climbed out of the trailer.

The new arrival was rather smelly.

"I fell in some cow's stuff," Thomas explained sadly. To his dismay, Elsie ran indoors to find some of Stumpy's old clothes for him to put on.

Whilst Stumpy unloaded the corn from Little Red Tractor's trailer, Thomas asked him some questions about his quad bike.

"Why don't you come and take a look," said Stumpy, taking Thomas around to the other side of the windmill.

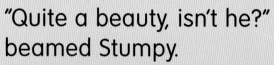

"Quite a beauty, isn't he?" beamed Stumpy.

"Brilliant!" agreed Thomas. Stumpy gave Nipper a proud pat, then headed back to the trailer.

Thomas thanked Stumpy, but there was a shock in store When he turned back to the quad bike, Nipper had rolled off the jacks!

"He's running away!" Thomas cried helplessly.

Thomas tore down the hill after Nipper, shouting at the top of his voice.

"Mr Stumpy! Your bike! Oh help… MR STUMPY!"

"Don't worry, Stumpy," said Stan, "Little Red Tractor will catch up with him!"

Little Red Tractor gave a determined toot, before speeding down the hill after Nipper.

Nipper was starting to gather speed by the time Stumpy, Ryan and Amy joined the chase.

"Come back!" shouted Stumpy who was running out of puff. Nipper had nearly reached Tawny Owl Wood.

At the bottom of the hill, Nipper finally wedged himself underneath a fallen tree trunk

He was followed a few seconds later by a very breathless Thomas.

Thomas used all his strength to try and heave the quad bike out from under the tree.

"Come… on… you…" he panted, falling back into the mud.

Nipper was stuck fast.

"Well Thomas, what happened here?" asked Stan, when he and Little Red Tractor arrived a moment later.

"I don't know! Nipper just rolled off," said Thomas, "and now he's stuck."

"We'll have to move that tree," Stan decided.

Thomas was flabbergasted. "Move the tree... how?"

"Little Red Tractor will give it a go!" said Stan.

Stan looped a strong length of rope round the tree trunk, then tied it to the front of Little Red Tractor.

"He's a lot stronger than he looks," explained Stan. "Stand clear, Thomas."

"The tree's moving!" gasped Thomas.

The tractor's spinning whe were splattering him with mu but Thomas didn't care how looked anymore.

Little Red Tractor held the tree clear of Nipper's bonnet, but the rope was starting to fray.

"Quick Stumpy!" cried Stan. "Get him out!"

Stumpy pulled Nipper out in the nick of time.

"It's all my fault," confessed Stumpy. "I must have loosened the brake cable when I was fixing the wheel."

"You were great, Little Red Tractor," said Thomas, giving him a friendly hug.

Back at Beech Farm, Mr Jones was enjoying a lunchtime snooze.

"Thomas? Good grief! What happened?" he spluttered when he woke up.

His nephew couldn't wait to tell him about his exciting morning in Babblebrook.

"And what's that terrible smell?" asked Mr Jones.

"That'll be me. Well the cows actually," laughed Thomas. "They're brilliant, but not as brilliant as Little Red Tractor!"